DEAR BISHOP

Dear Bishop

by
CATHERINE
de
HUECK

SHEED and WARD
New York

Manufactured in the United States of America
By The Haddon Craftsmen, Inc., Scranton, Pa.

To my mother

FOREWORD

During the war an assignment was given to me by a member of the Hierarchy in America. The assignment was to find out what American youth, working, and in the armed forces of this country, thought of God, His Church, Churches in general; what was their reaction to Communism and Democracy. So I went to work for many months as factory hand and waitress, living on my earnings as the poorest live. What I went through brought back to me my first years in America when I *had* to work like that, not to study social trends but to keep from starving. The two experiences somehow fused into one experience, and out of it this book grew. The writer of the letters, Katzie, is not any one real person: call her fictional: but she is the only fictional thing in the book.

FIRST LETTER

Dear Bishop

Do you ever receive letters from one of your flock—as things go, a very unimportant one at that? A mere working woman, one of the "masses"? You "meet" the likes of me from far, far away, when you bless us at some function we have come to attend and where we are always to be found at the outskirts of the crowd, for we are usually too shabby to be at the front of it. Or again you "see" us at some solemn service of the Church. Yes, we meet you like that at a distance. And you look kind.

It just came to me in my dark, shabby, hopeless little room on a slummy street of a big city, this desire to write you a letter. Perhaps I shall write others . . . maybe many. It might help to keep me sane, to chase the blues away, to still the deep voice of confusion, almost despair, that

1

shouts so loudly in my ears, as it does in the ears of countless others like me. For we who live in the backyards of our cities have no one to talk to; no one to answer the thousand questions that crowd one another in our tired brains.

Anyhow there are lost sheep down here, plenty. Sure they ought to come to you, but that's what a lost sheep is—one that has lost all idea of finding the shepherd. Who is going to go after us? Somewhere long ago I read that pastors are "fathers of their flock." Being a member of that flock, I don't see why I should not write to my father. Do you? I still can afford the price of a stamp once in a while, if the night takings are good and the "girls" got enough customers drunk to give me my tips. But about that later.

I am not going to bother you with my autobiography, except to say that I have seen better days and have had some schooling, and that I write these letters not for myself alone, but for the millions of other lost sheep, who would never dream of writing to you—as well as for the working women, young, middle-aged and even old, whom no one notices, for the working man

2

and his family, and especially the kids of our big cities in and out of the armed services.

I see them all, night after night, in the cheap taverns and saloons of the large cities where I have been and still am, waiting on them, bringing them endless glasses of beer, Calverts and cokes, whiskeys with beer chasers, watching them trying to escape, trying to forget and ending in being more confused than ever. Yes, it is for all of us that I am writing. Not expecting an answer, not even giving you my address. Just writing to my father, telling him, clumsily perhaps, but sincerely, how some of his children live, work and feel.

You have the words of eternal life and they could answer all that confusion and misery, but we don't seem to hear them down here. Yes I know. There is the Church. The Mass. The Sacraments. We need them and you give them to us—if we come for them. But what about those of us who don't come, who are too tired, or too discouraged, or too far gone in sin? Our Lord said, "Leave the ninety-nine, and go after the sheep that is lost." It sometimes seems to me that the figures should be the other way round.

One OK, ninety-nine lost. But maybe that comes from working where I do, in cheap joints on shoddy streets.

Yet, we are so hungry, so bewildered, so lost. True, somehow we manage to look after the body (not always though)—watching every penny, eating the wrong food. We exist at least, if we do not die from "hidden hunger" or the White Death. But what of the mind, the heart, the soul? Oh! the hunger of the multitudes!

I go to church Sunday. Yes, I still do. Because somehow I still love and believe in God. I manage to get there just when the Gospel is read. I finish serving drinks at three, Sunday morning. If I rush, I can make it. But I never feel that anybody is interested in the things that are bothering the likes of me. What of justice? What of fair wages? What of real Charity, whose other name is love? What of tomorrow, when all this mess is over? Will there be bread lines, WPA's, welfare queues again? What of the cold hate that is growing in our hearts? What of the answers to a better world for everyone—here and now?

Sure, I know, it's the social system that's broken down, not the Church. The Church isn't a Universal Aunt mending everybody else's messes. But the breakdown of the social system is making hell for thousands of us and making Faith terribly hard. We need all the contact with the shepherd we can get. And he'll have to make the contact. Most of us don't even try. We're lost . . . or half lost anyway.

But I am running ahead of myself. In this first letter, I was going to give you a little word picture of our Way of the Cross, the Worker's Way . . . each step of it an agony all its own! So here goes, for a little story of what happens to a woman and some girls when they come to a big city, like this one. And did you know that with the War on, they come in droves? For in almost every paper in the country, little alluring ads tell us that this or that city is the working-man's paradise just now.

New York, where I come from isn't a war town. Folks leave it for better places. One of them is supposed to be your city. So women and girls pack cheap suitcases, slave for a fare, and, taking overcrowded trains or buses, sit up all night—

maybe several nights and days—and finally reach their goal. I did. And so did Marie, a kid who waited in a Sixth Avenue joint in New York. And Rosie, who was a "bus girl" in a cheap restaurant in Little Italy—also New York. We all chummed up on the way. Funny too, we were all three of us Catholic. I had been here before. They were strangers to this city. We talked things over on the way, and decided that the best place to start from would be the center of the town. There ought to be a church there.

We could inquire about things. So when we got to the station, we had a cup of coffee and made for the Traveler's Aid. The lady of same told us there were two Catholic churches in the business district, and gave us their addresses. We checked our suitcases and hoofed it to the nearest one. The kids waited in the church and I went and rang the bell of the rectory.

The housekeeper was in a hurry, looking as if it would hurt her to talk. I guess she was worn out with people like me. "Rooms in our parish," she replied to my query, "I don't know of any. There is a Catholic Room Registry somewhere. You better go to the Catholic Charities. They'll tell you all about it. Here is their address. Good day to you." Then the housekeeper gave me some mumbled direction as to how to get to the Catholic Charities. But what the heck! We were all tired out and wanted a place—any place —to wash and rest for a while. So, standing by the rectory, we looked North and South. North looked all business places. South had some houses. We went South. Sure enough, one block from the church, we found it—a dirty grey stone house with a "Rooms for rent—vacancies" sign on the door.

Everyone who has to deal with the poor ought to live a month in one of those graves of all human hope and decency—a rooming house on a rundown street. They would be wiser and more understanding then. Marie and Rosie did not like the looks of the place and so left me. I have not seen them since, these chance young companions of mine. The city has swallowed them. Where will she vomit them, awhile hence? On the dump heap? I don't hesitate to mention them, because they are the sheep He died for.

I took the room. I was too tired to look further, and so what have I got for four fifty a week?

What does *any* woman or girl get when, weary, strange, and done in, she lands in a big, sprawling, busy city, looking for the elusive will-of-the-wisp, a better economic break? I'll tell you. She gets a room papered in dirty brown or dirty green. The walls all marked and stained, the wallpaper cracked. A cheap brown dresser with the first drawer missing stands crookedly against the wall. The mirror strangely distorts a tired face. Sloppy curtains hang limply on a dingy window. A double bed, with a saggy mattress and broken springs, sports a dirty blanket, and houses bed bugs. A few nails on the wall with a brown rag for a coverage—that is her clothes closet. The carpet, what there is left of it, sticks to the feet, from sheer dirt. The little bulb in an overhead lamp makes everything worse and forbids any reading. There are many rooms in this house, just like mine. They rent by the day. The night. The week and the month. *And people live in them. . . .*

But who cares anyhow? It is close to the business section and saves at least carfare. And I don't know the city, or anyone in it yet. One room is as good as another to me to sleep in when I don't work.

For a whole day, I just lay there and stared at the walls—the dirty brown walls—too tired to move. Too tired to take up the endless grind with so little hope for anything *real* . . . and yet my whole soul cried out to the Lord—"*Why, why? why does no one care . . . doesn't care at all what happens to me . . where I go . . what I do . . me . . and thousands like me. . . . And yet, You, Lord, died for me . . for the likes of me, too . . . didn't You?*"

Only when you lie there in a dirty, brown room, when you should be looking for a job to get your next meal from . . . *God seems mighty far away* . . . and maybe the thought comes to you: *There isn't any God. . . . After all; surely if there were . . . ?*

"Knock," He said, "and it will be opened to you. Ask and you shall receive." Well I knocked . . and got me a room on a dingy, lousy street for my knocking . . and I have asked for a long time for a break, a friendly place, a friendly hand . . and I am lying alone, staring at a dirty ceiling and writing you . . because I just feel like going nuts if I don't.

9

Sure enough, there is another "Marie" on my left, and another "Rosie" on my right, even if their names respectively are Jean and Imelda. Well Jean was crying this morning, soft-like. So I went into her room and she told me, in answer to my question, that last night she got herself a man and slept with him. A stranger.

And Jean 19 or 20 only. And her soldier husband in Africa or some such place, and she a Catholic of sorts too. An orphan she is. From a little town in Indiana. She met her man, a bus driver, while she was a waitress in a road lunch-house. They fell in love. Married. The draft got him. He was sent here. She joined him. Soon they took him away. She gets the wife's allowance. Lives in this dump, too frightened, too bewildered to exert herself to something better. No kith nor kin. She is just lonesome. No place to go. Got herself a job slinging hash again in a joint nearby. That's her life. The restaurant—and her dirty brown room. She just broke. Needed a little loving, a little companionship . . . got it . . . a strange man in her bed.

What can be done about the Jeans, Imeldas, Rosies, Maries, of our big cities? Those little kids with a couple of vulgar, showy dresses to their names, a pack of chewing gum . . a ready, snappy answer by day and soft tears by night? Who is taking care of those "lost lambs" for the Lord who died for them too? They can't (and won't) join sodalities . . and if they did—the "good" girls would not accept them. They have not been taught how. The young curates in charge would not feel at home with these kids, either. Their views aren't wholesome. Neither is their language. It goes with being lost!

Imelda on my right, was a Catholic too. But at twenty-three she has gone through it all. Had the "blues," the "brownies." Knows "the ropes of the world" all right. Doesn't seem to have any idea of the ropes of God. She does not care. Why should she? She has plenty of fun . . men . . drinks . . cheap jewelry . . and flashy clothes. One thing I don't get, why does she still keep a picture of our Blessed Mother over her bed?

Well, I guess I'll close my first letter to you Father. Time to go and look for a job. All I had was a couple of javas and an oatmeal today. A body can't live on that. So here goes . . and afterwards . . a job, a dirty brown room . . and millions of unanswered questions to take to bed with me. I dropped into the church in the next block today . . and saw a picture of Our Lord. I still think *He cares and understands. So I'll look for that job and stick around for a little while longer. . . .*

SECOND LETTER

Dear Bishop

Here I am again. I knew that I could not stop writing to you, once I had begun. It is as if I were speaking for the multitudes who will never speak to you for themselves. What will come out of this writing, I don't know. All I know is that my conscience will be at peace. The rest is up to God! I can do no more than tell.

It helps me too. For my room is still dark, dirty and kind of hopeless—the mirror of a life. Many lives. The light blue curtains I got the other day for a few cents, in the bargain basement of a big store, have not helped at all. In fact they only emphasize the general drabness of the place. . . .

It is tough to look for a job. Really "look," because the $1.75 in your purse is so little to live on. Because Wednesday (or any other day for that matter) stands out from the rest of the week-days, in letters of fire—*rent day*. Four fifty on the nail, or you will not even have the dubious shelter of your brown room to come home to . . . Then what? The ghastly choice between organized charity, so "un-charitable," so scientific, so cold . . or men to sleep with . . who at least have a kind word to say.

Why is it, Bishop, that the so-called lost souls, sinners, so often have real true warm charity toward the poor? Why is it that if and when they give—their giving is so delicate and gracious in its very direct simplicity? More "sharing" than giving. And why, on the other hand, is the giving of the GOOD, the ones in the state of grace, so often condescending, so cold and bitter to take? Reminds me of the time I was broke in New York City, and had to sleep in a mission on the Bowery. . . .

I can still see its neon sign blinking radiantly against a dark, sleety night. "Jesus saves" the sign kept saying. The name alone spelled sweetness and hope, both were absent within. The walls were a forbidding, dark, dismal gray. The woman at the desk reflected the same mood. Wordlessly she handed me a key and pointed upward. At the top of the stairs, another, just as forbidding met me. Curtly she ordered me to disrobe, put my clothes in a closet and take a shower. And while I was doing so, the water and her voice ran in unison, urging me to "repent," to become "decent" again. But, Bishop, I was decent. Or is poverty a sin? The soap smelled of carbolic, the woman's voice was carbolic acid too, a monotone of preaching. Yet every word left a deep wound, that in turn has left deep scars. I have them yet. Who will heal these?

A tier bunk. Rough, prickly blankets. Prison-like atmosphere. Not a smile. Not a kind word along the way. At four-thirty A.M.—OUT— without breakfast, into the cold raw city dawn. Yet the sign still blinked against it, throwing rhythmically pools of light against its murky darkness, spelling and re-spelling the sweetest Name in the world . . *The name of the Man-God Who so loved sinners that He died for them.* Yes— L O V E it is that seems to get squeezed out of most organized charities—*that must be why they are so hard to accept.*

But I wander again. I meant to tell you of my *today,* not of my dismal yesterdays! I was going to tell you of getting jobs. I was going to explain how easy the path to evil is made for a working woman or girl, and how hard the path to virtue. Take many of the agencies in a big city. They look you over first when you apply for a menial or manual job. Your chances and pay check go up if you happen to have a good form and face.

Shades of the old slave markets! Flesh for sale again—streamlined style. Waitresses, chambermaids, tavern girls—pulchritude *first*, dexterity *next*. One is sold a night job first. The line runs as follows: "Men go there, you will have good tips." All this with a smirk and a knowing look. How long must we stand for this? How long must we take it? We "take it" all the time. Often I have felt as if I never could wash off the filth thrown at my womanhood in search of jobs.

So much down. So much per week. You pay for being given a job, even one that will barely provide the necessities of life. And you pay plenty. Or you did until recently. And you will again. As soon as the war is over. Oh, for a Christian agency, a Catholic one for me! Where I could be greeted with a smile, where the dignity of my humanity would be recognized! I am so weary.

16

SECOND LETTER

My feet are tired walking the cold pavement. I am sick at heart. My brain is in a constant whirl. Loneliness hems me in on all sides. In the busy street. In my hopeless room. A loneliness that kills.

But I made the agencies. Listening to the old, old line; in modern slang this time. "Sure, girlie, I am telling you it's a swell joint. Plenty of good customers. Men mostly; and do they go for dames like you! That means tips. Take that night job. Better pickings. . . ." And for this so much down, and a week's pay. I wasn't having any. The manpower shortage was not yet in full swing, but I chucked the agencies and went on my own, striking pay dirt at once, as it were.

A "cocktail lounge"—the modern name for a saloon—displayed a large sign "Waitress Wanted." It wasn't exactly a paradise, being on a dingy, dusty, backwash street, but it was clean did not smell too badly for all its dimness, lack of ventilation, and the deafening noise that came from a boogey-woogey orchestra.

Fifteen minutes later, I was hired to start the next day, Saturday. Did you ever experience that strange sense of relief that comes from knowing that there is a job and that YOU have it, and that at least the hopeless room will be paid for and some sort of food will be there to give you strength?

True, this sense of relief will soon pass in the endless monotony of jobs like mine. Other needs will come, clamoring loudly to be filled. Need of wholesome recreation, of companionship, clean and pleasant, of opportunities to better oneself. Spiritual, mental, emotional needs. Yes, all of these will soon crowd upon you. But for the time being, all you know is relief, that you will have a place to sleep, something to eat, something to do.

Saturday came. And 6 P.M. too, bringing with it the saloon. New people to get acquainted with. A boss to be measured. Co-workers to be estimated. A new job to get used to. But that does not take over long for people like me who have been earning their living that way for years. Yet I could not help feeling anew, how each job of this kind is a world unto itself. Fast bound, apart, yet somehow correlated, integrated with other little worlds around it. A

chain of many links, a beehive which the soci-
ologists delight in calling the "working masses,"
or the proletariat.

Come, Bishop, let me take you into *my* little cell
of that world—the old saloon, whose hair has
now a permanent and whose face has been lifted
in the year of grace 1943. Come and see for yourself, how some of the ninety-nine sheep live that
seem to be forgotten by all.

Remember that this cell of mine caters to thousands of others, who do not work there, but for
whom *it works*. Soldiers, sailors, Marines and
Air Corps. Men and women, who find in it what
they seem unable to get anywhere else—a modicum of peace, a place to talk and have bull sessions in, unsupervised, uncensored. Companionship of their own kind and choice—not carefully
selected for them by others. Those others who
seem to have, somehow, forgotten the realities
of living. Yes, my little cell—the rejuvenated
saloon of old—is a world of its own—a world in
which God's voice just doesn't get heard.

The old bar is still there. Glistening and highly
polished. The brass rail is gone. High stools

with multicolored, vivid leather coverings have replaced it. The bottles still stand, shining, not against a fly-specked mirror but against fancy lights. The bartender is the same tough guy he used to be, but has now a new line of talk . . . and will oblige the public on occasion, by singing in a deep bass—"Moonlight becomes you so. . . ." Yet he still can revert to type and throw a drunk out with the same brutal efficiency that his father knew.

Besides dispensing drinks, he is also the purveyor of the latest "snappy story." Addresses of "hot numbers" are his stock in trade too, and maybe he gets a rake-off from them. Nor is he above earning an extra penny in selling contraceptives on the sly, or a potency remedy. Otherwise he is just what he seems—a bartender.

Yet, Bishop, some of them are Catholics by birth. Once in a while their disillusioned eyes light with a strange light, when they talk of their youth and the days when they were altar boys. Yet, almost always these reminiscences end in— "I was a sucker then. I know better now. Religion is just another racket. Only you've got to be smart to get into it. But, boy, if you do, the shekels just roll in."

The bar room floozy is no more. Her modern sister is another creature. She looks like a "lady" until she opens her mouth. And sometimes even after that. Some have graduated from colleges. Would it surprise you very much, Bishop, that these include Catholic colleges? In some cities they are called "B-girls;" in others, "party-girls," or "cocktail-girls." But what's in a name? Their job holds regular union hours—eight—though they belong to no union. Not a minute longer will they "work." They get no salaries from the management. They don't need salaries. They make enough without it. Their duty is to approach every male customer who comes into the tavern, and ask, beg, or cajole him into buying them "a drink." If the gent says—go ahead—they will ask for "a shot," or "a pinch bottle."

"A shot" is a whiskey glass full of colored water or root beer (both look like the real McCoy) with a water chaser. A "pinch bottle" is the same, only there is a drop or two of real whiskey on top, so that the weary or wary customer may smell it and be fooled a little longer into buying more drinks. The price of these is regular—forty-five cents. Clear profit, as you see—for the house. The girl does not drink it anyhow. She spits it back into the water chaser—most skill-fully, and gets twenty cents on each "drink." It mounts up, Bishop, it mounts up, if you know what I mean. The girls' takes are often $50 a week, or over.

But this is not all. The story starts at the bar. Sometimes it ends there. More often it continues in a booth. It is purposely dark, in the modern rejuvenated saloon, Bishop. So dark that men and women can "make love" to one another. All things are permitted (more or less depend-ing on the locality) except cohabitation, Bishop, in these booths. The girl's next step is to sell real liquor to him, root beer to herself, but at a higher price. Her body is offered in the sale. For now the man may, for forty-five cents a shot, fondle, caress, and kiss her for hours—so long as his cash holds out.

Being pawed by Tom, Dick, and Harry gets on one's nerves, even on those of a "B-girl." So, to be able to stand it, she orders in between "shots" —the real stuff. But what the hell! A girl has a right to some real stuff in that racket. What if she does not get a cut on it? It gives her courage to go through with the "union hours." Don't

you think, Bishop, straight prostitution **is**
cleaner?

Soon or later, bar girls "hook up" with a customer. Usually he is the type that will not only
allow her to keep her "job," but encourage her
to continue it. For he will live henceforth "off
her pickings." Often, driven to nausea by her
evening work, she will agree to go "cabareting"
with an older, cleaner man—one who happened
to drop in, that evening. This will always end
in the same thing—for money, or not, as the
spirit moves her—and a next-morning hang-
over, for she has been drinking this time—*the
real stuff. And plenty of it.*

The end of a "B-girl?" Well, it depends. At best,
she will marry and buy herself a tavern, be a
good boss—for she sure knows all the answers.
She ought to. She has given the best years of her
life to find them. At worst, she will be found by
the Church in a social disease ward or a hospital
for the insane. Or again, she might be picked
up by the Catholic Charities or State organiza-
tions as a "case." Funny, isn't it (if one can
laugh), that no one bothered with the "B-girl"
while she was in the bar? Young, pliant, with

memories of her childhood still undimmed by the boogey-woogey noises of modern orchestras, not yet degraded by the hungry eager hands of men on her shapely body or by faked or real drinks,—that child might have been reclaimed, did anyone care to reclaim her.

Why not then, start on her at the beginning? Why only at the end? Christ died for her too . . . or did He? At times I seem to lose the answer. Maybe He never was? Or maybe *He was just a dream*. For where I work and where I live, there is never anything to remind me of *Him*!

The B-girl is wrapped in anonymity. Yes. For all except the tight little world of those who work in a saloon. For us they are human beings. With brothers, mothers, families, heartaches, homes of sorts, laughter and tears. We know their homey little happenings—like the new kitten Loise got. She called it "her baby." Wistfully. Or Ginette's tears when she heard that her brother lost his leg in Guadalcanal. Or Grace's worrying about her mother "who does not know," and lives in an Eastern town. Yes, they are human. AND OH SO IMPORTANT, girls in bars. The loneliest creatures in the world. Pathetically hungry for simple, homey things. For friendship, understanding, clean companionship. Yes full of another hunger too, one they don't know about, but which makes them restless. Hunger for God. Full, also of a strange philosophy, all their own. Full of *Charity*. Delicate, spontaneous and terribly real. I hope that God has a very special place in heaven for them. Cosy, simple, and full of flowers and the sunshine they never saw in the bars, taverns, and cocktail lounges of America.

Take Grace. She lives with several other "respectable girls," and she works in our bar in the daytime, because she does not want her friends, nor her family "to know what type of work" she does. If she goes "cabareting," she dutifully phones that she is going out of town for a day or two—on business. Grace went to a Catholic college. She went to a Catholic grade and high school. How many years of Catholic training is that?

The old story is Grace's. She fell in love with a divorced man. She thought there might be something wrong with his first marriage, that maybe he could get a decree of nullity. Went to see a priest to find if there was a way out. The priest did not even bother to look it up. He just "threw her out on her ear." That's her story anyhow. I haven't heard the priest's side of it. Blinded with pain, yet Catholic enough to realize that "marriage" under the circumstances would be a farce, she went to live with the man. In the raw, as she puts it. Eventually they parted. She drifted . . . until she came to port in a bar.

Perhaps it was the great love that was in my heart for all of them. Or the pity I could not keep out of my eyes. But whatever it was—they "talked" to me. It is so hard, Bishop, to make them talk, yet it is good for them. Grace told me that I made her think of her childhood just by being around. "What is it about you, Polack," she said, "that shines?" I could not tell her that it was love and pity, could I? I was only the hired help around there. That is all. Anyhow, Grace talked. Told me, that come every Lent, she felt that "drag" back to Church. . . . That once in a while she would just "sneak into one," if only to "look at the Lord." Yet she ended up—"Who the hell cares about me? What is the use? Give me a real scotch, Polack, and no chaser."

What she did was all wrong. I know that. Yet that is the definition of a lost sheep. But someone has to go after the lost sheep. Who will take time out to talk to Grace? Who will be there when she wants to "talk" about God again? Who will someday go to Mass with her? To what priest can she be taken, and who is to take her? Who will love Grace enough to spend his life in saloons where there are thousands of other Graces? *Who? . . . Who . . . ? Who . . . ?*

Ginette is half Italian and half Irish. Well Ginette is through. That is, humanly speaking, she is lost for good. As far as eyes can see anyhow. I dare not even tell you what has ended her religion. And yet her very bitterness and hate of it, are only symptoms of the depth of her hurt.

Loise the beautiful, doll-like girl, who stole cheap pretties when she was four. A product of the East Side of a large city. Loise of the charitable heart. Lover of poor kids, cats and dogs. Can nothing be done for her?

Martha, the level-headed, who someday wants to be "respectable again." Marie who wears our

Lady's Medal because her dying mother put it around her neck, and who once in a while talks laughingly of the days when she was such a damn fool that she thought of being a *nun* . . . then quickly produces her "Black Book," and reads out of it the filthiest story she can find and laughs hard and long at it. Yet that laughter of hers is both empty and forced. Gwendolyne . . Jean . . Helene. And many more. In every city of the Union. Every night all over these towns. Women, many of whom have been baptised IN THE NAME OF THE FATHER, THE SON, AND THE HOLY GHOST . . . *in the true faith* . . . are on their way to work union hours at losing their souls. The souls *God died for*!

As I walk my endless miles on the floor of my tavern, calling out the never ending roll of— "one beer, three Calverts and cokes . . one shot for Grace, and an H & H for her gent," I keep hoping that you will find some way of bringing *help to us, the undiscovered home missions of today* . . Good night Bishop. It is time to finish this letter, time to keep a strange date *with the Forgotten Christ . . . in a saloon.*

THIRD LETTER

Dear Bishop

I am now working in a factory. Got tired of the boogey-woogey noise, and changed my job. I'll be back there yet, for the money is better there than elsewhere, and I need money so badly . . . But those tunes, for eight hours straight, get me. It's like listening to dance music with a corpse in the house.

Here we are at war. Thousands die daily . . . on battlefields. While others get ready either to get there, or to let someone they love get there. Here we are . . . saloons, taverns, burlesque shows, and what have you . . selling forgetfulness to the tune of slow blues, or lustful swing. Me, what worries me, is that I keep thinking that not only bodies are dying, but souls in America too. Because so many people, who might do something about it, don't know (maybe don't even care to know), what is cooking under the seemingly smooth surface of living. Yes, that is it . . I quit for a while . . to get a change.

I got less money to start with. They pay you twenty-one a week to look after five machines that make paper cups for the Army and for civilians. Figure it out for yourself. Four-fifty for the room. Fifty cents for the man of all work there, or life will be hell. That's five a week. You have to eat out, and at the present prices, figure a dollar fifty a day. You can of course "live" on one dollar a day for three meals out— but you won't live long. That's ten dollars a week for food. And five is fifteen. Carfare takes another dollar. Union dues fifty cents. Take the taxes—Victory and Social Security out, and your pay check is really $18 and some cents. And there you are. Sixteen-fifty out of eighteen and some cents leaves you a couple of bucks for clothing, soap, recreation, doctors, dentists, hospital insurance, cosmetics, and what have you. Nothing to splurge on, believe me. Nothing to write home about. So to make ends meet— after all—you do spend on food, a dollar a day or so. That is the way of it.

The job is a rush job, so you stand on your feet
for eight hours, watching the machine make the
cups, endlessly vomiting them out in neat rows
of a hundred. Catch them . . . pack them . . .
before the next inexorable hundred pops out.
You've got to work fast with five machines, so
fast that after a while you kind of figure you are
part of a machine yourself. The noise beats in
your brain . . . until you can't think. Your hands
move automatically, with a rhythm all their
own, in tune with the beat of the machine . . .
another boogey-woogey of today.

Rest periods. Every two hours for ten minutes.
A little longer time for midnight lunch. For the
place works on three shifts. Girls, women, forty
of them on each shift on my floor. They gather
around a radio, to smoke and to chew the rag.
Maybe you'd like to know that out of the forty,
twenty-two are Catholics, or should be. Out of
these only *four* go to church. *Four out of twenty-
two* . . . so eighteen have got lost along the way.

The mechanic is talking about the Communists.
About what a swell set-up Russia has, and of the
break that a worker gets there. Free insurance,
medicine, and plenty of free time. It may be all

untrue for all I know. But there is always some-one around to put the case for Russia!

Everyone listens, just like kids listen to a fairy story . . . eyes shining, lips parted. One of the four Catholics timidly ventures a remark about athe-ism. Quick as flash the mechanic retorts, "Or-ganized religion, girlie? Why that is a wet spot, a dirty wet spot at that, that God would not step on for fear of dirtying His feet." And he goes on at length telling them that no Church, least of all the Roman Catholic, has "stood by the worker" through the depression, or in his grand fight for social justice in the USA . . . that the Hierarchy has sided all along with the vested interests, that they stand firm and sure with the status quo . . . that they are rich in holdings, bonds, stocks, mortgages, real estate . . . espe-cially in the slum areas. "Landlords to the poor," he spits out, "squeeze the last penny outa you." Someone mentions the Pope's letters on Labor, and back comes the snappy answer, "Yea, sure; those guys in Rome wrote good stuff. But you tell me, is it preached in their snooty churches?"

I feel in my bones that all this is untrue. But I haven't got the facts, and none of the Catholics here have any answer either. It is going on all the time. If only there was someone around to teach us the answers! The machine resumes its exhausting song . . . fingers automatically work, separating, packing, checking. My heart is full of pain. I feel like crying. A great darkness comes over me. What's the use? The voice of truth doesn't sound down here. Can't something be done?

I did not see the fellow, nor hear him. Yet the next thing I knew he had grabbed me from behind, his callous hands jokingly, yet sickeningly "exploring" my body. I was unprotected because my hands were full of paper cups. Lewd remarks float in the air . . . an unclean laughter rises above the machine song. Anger floods me. I drop the paper cups and shout, "Keep your dirty hands off me—you slug."

It's the foreman. He leers, makes an obscene gesture and goes away shouting, "Keep your shirt on, baby." More than ever I want to cry, but tears won't come. And what is the use anyhow? The girl next to me bends over and whispers loudly, "Don't kick too much kid . . . or you ain't got a job. He is that way. They all are, you know." Damn! Of course, I know. I have known it ever since I started working at 18. Now I can quit. There are plenty of jobs. But a few years ago when there weren't any? Sure, it is hard to say "no" to the guys who hold our bread, never mind the butter.

Maybe you are shocked, for the Church preaches in season and out of it—the sixth Commandment. The preaching is fine, only life can be pretty tough. Take it this way—here I am getting twenty-one bucks a week on an ever-rising cost of living. I could do with thirty—eat better, live better on it. Yet it is a job. And the guy with the greedy hands and the dirty mind, the foreman, can fire or keep me. If I "behave" . . . I've got to eat haven't I? Maybe he or some other guy will stake me to a *real* meal once in a while. Girls are often hungry. Honestly, it isn't easy to be virtuous on an empty stomach. Take it from me. Look, I live in an eternal fear of sickness . . . for that means a week off without pay, without money to pay the doctors. It means a city or county hospital. Have you ever been through that? Waiting. Coming back to the clinic. Waiting some more. No, perhaps you would not understand. It would be easier to keep the sixth Commandment if I could be dead sure that those who preach it knew what it cost people like us to keep it.

Here we are, night after night, forty people gathered together for a little space of time. A Gallup poll of American workers, 11 nationalities. We stand around a radio in a factory, to talk over things that matter so much to us, and therefore, to all the workers in this country and in the rest of the world. Does anyone listen in? No, no one but the Communists bother. The press, for the freedom of which we are supposed to fight, would not touch us with a ten-foot pole, for we are not "important" people. Not "news." So why bother? People don't want to read anything about other people with funny foreign names, unless they are dukes or millionaires. Yet in the midst of silent machines on dirty floors littered with paper-scraps, the soul and mind of a nation is being bared.

Restless, worried, frightened, angry workers talk in many factories . . . wondering about many things. Mostly about "tomorrow," and what it'll bring. As far as they are concerned, it had better bring them freedom from want . . . or else . .

They'll go after it—fighting. They say that revolution is on its way . . . that it is here . . . that it might turn bloody any minute now, and for sure, if they don't get what is due them. Decent living. Fair wages. Protection against sickness and death. They are not going back to WPA's, NYA's, Welfare lines. *No siree. . . . Take it from me . . . they just ain't.* Rivers of blood may well flow before they do. They are fed up and then some, with the run-around they have been given. Thus they talk.

Maybe that's all talk. Just pathetic. Maybe they'll never be anything but underdogs. Maybe they haven't the stuff in them to make a revolution. But that is what they talk about around the radio, munching cheap soggy sandwiches from the joint downstairs, drinking it down with coffee. They "don't trust nobody," they say—just now. They are sore at the Administration for "selling them down the river." They are sore at the food muddle—"dirty muddle," they call it. Sore at the rising cost of living. They feel a strange solidarity in their minds with *all* workers of the world. They are super champions of China and Russia. Especially Russia. They use long-winded words to explain their needs. They are angry, deeply angry, at their memories of the depression. And you know they tell over and over again how the Communists stood by them during it—*their only friends*!

The Church? It is just not in the picture, in their minds. It had no place in their *yesterday*, so they have shoved it completely (or almost so) out of the *tomorrow*. They say it was not there when they hungered and wept, so it will have no right to be there when they die for the right not to hunger any more. They do not even pay the Church the compliment of considering it a worthy foe. And they are young. Funny that neither press, nor Church, nor government, nor anyone I know of, is interested in what the workers of America, its youth, either in or out of the Armed Forces, *really, truly think* . . . and *how* they think! No one except the Communists and perhaps some hidden fascist groups. Funny. So funny, I sort of want to jump in the lake and end it all *now*, before I lose my faith.

I guess I will have to quit this place soon. For the pay check, not being of rubber, does not stretch out far enough. I have been kind of hungry this week, and tired. My room is more hopeless than ever. I am too tired to walk the streets, even to do some window shopping—never mind going to a cheap show. I haven't got the money, and to hell with men that can pay for a feed and a picture. A girl has got to pay back for that too. It's all screwy . . . or seems to be.

I keep hearing over and over again . . . the agonizing words . . "My God, my God, why hast Thou forsaken me?" Somehow, tonight, they seem to belong to me too!

FOURTH LETTER

Dear Bishop

So I quit the factory. Just too hungry to stay on. Twenty-one bucks a week, which became a little more than $18 in the pay envelope, kept me so hungry I could not keep on working. Funny ain't it, that so many people are still hungry in this land of plenty—in peace or war? But who cares anyhow?

You probably think I change jobs too quickly, but then so would anyone else if she were me. For the likes of us are always looking for new jobs that will add a dollar or two and give us a margin. Allow us the strange, funny joy of paying for a movie ourselves, of buying that special pair of stockings we fancied so, or a knick-knack for that drab room, without depending on a "man" to get it for us.

Have you ever heard the lilt in the voice of Loise, Ginette, or the others when they point to some little thing and smilingly say, "I bought it all myself." Everyone around knows exactly what they are talking about . . . and sort of smiles too. That is what I mean. But most of the time, the everlasting change of jobs does not bring any lilt into our voices, for it never quite brings us enough to cover the bare necessities.

So I quit the factory . . . and now I am a chambermaid in a hotel run by a Christian organization—of all places. Did you ever see its letters of fire, on top of the building, glare against a dark night sky? It is there. Strangely the lights blend with sounds for me. Sounds of marching feet, and lusty martial songs. And the two contradict and exclude each other. All through the days, and the nights, passing my windows, youth marches. Soldiers in training, singing as they go, to the sharp dry cry of the sergeant "hep . . . hep . . . hep." Marching feet and song in cadence never allow one to forget that there is a war on, and the flower of our manhood is dying in some distant land. The red letters blink to a rhythm too, out of tune with that other. Do you notice the "Christian" in it? Let us take it out of there. It really does not belong. Christ, I know, would not tolerate it there.

Let me tell you why. The housekeeper's room, like all rooms in the place, is cozy with chintz and period furniture out of a department store. She herself appears prim, proper and righteous. There seems to be a slight touch of contempt for me. But she needs help. The ad says so. "Young women and housewives—attractive jobs open as chambermaids. Six hours a day. Top pay."

Six hours a day. Top pay. Eye wash, Bishop. I worked as chambermaid in hotels—regular ones. At most I had to do 10 or 12 rooms for $60 a month and lunch. Here they offer me forty-five beds a day to make and $62 without lunch. But I have spent the wages from the factory. Wednesday, rent day, is nigh again. So I take the bally job then and there. At nine-thirty, I am on the floor, with a score of other women. Mostly Polish. Some Irish. Young, middle-aged, and even elderly. Some strangers to the city, for whom this job is a stop-gap.

We start. Checking linen. Making beds. More

beds. At top speed. Only six hours to make them in. Dust, mop rooms, throw trash out, push the vacuum. Faster . . . faster . . . ever faster. Bending, straightening out to bend again. Strong, trained muscles refuse to work. They cry out in pain. Feet hurt. Head swims. But there are only six hours to work! *And Wednesday is rent day*. Faster . . . faster. Sheets, blankets, pillowcases, counterpanes. Smooth tight on beds that begin to look like monsters.

The women's faces (and my own) begin to show lines of fatigue. Perspiration drenches our clothing. Dust settles on our hair, faces and hands. Faster . . . faster. Ah! the lunch bell. We have all of thirty little minutes to eat the sandwiches we brought, and wash them down with some tea we made, or just the water from the tap. The windows are open, the chintz curtains sway gently in the breeze. From the streets marching feet and young voices blend. "The caissons are rolling along." There is a war on. A war for what? The women stop eating. They lift their weary faces and fold their work-worn hands. One says, as if to herself, "I have two there." Another answers, "And I have one." Then they speak all at once, for almost every one of them, these modern economic slaves, has someone "over there." Tell me, Bishop, what are their menfolks fighting for? So that these women will be free to kill themselves working? Sure some of them get allowances from the Government for their men. But often their sons are married, and part of the money goes to the wife and kiddies. Then again, and often, the allowance is not enough. Believe me, not one of these women would work as she does . . . if she did not have to.

But the semi-genteel voice of the housekeeper calls me. "Katzie, Katzie, come here a moment, please." I enter the clean room to see her eat a full lunch from a well-served tray. She wants to explain to me that she does not need my social security number because their organization is tax exempt. That means that the meagre security which the Government guarantees me in a period of unemployment, by taxing employee and employer under the Social Security Act, is here denied me. "You see, Katzie," she adds, "You are really working for Christ!"

Bitterness, and such anger as I did not know I was capable of shakes me in a spasm. Her face grows until it is a blob, obscuring the light of the day. Mother of God! Christ of the Beatitudes! "Blessed are they that hunger for justice . . . they shall be filled." Hold me tight. I am losing my soul. Yes. Right this minute. I cannot go on. My back aches. My swollen feet burn in my shoes. I am still hungry, and oh so tired! *I cannot take this any more. . . .*

"The caissons are rolling along." No it is the voice of a mob that shouts, "Crucify Him . . . crucify Him." No it is not a mob either. It is the voice of a woman in a cheery, chintzy room, sitting before a well-filled tray, explaining to *me*, that in the name of the God Who died to make me free . . . to give me a break . . . she will take away the pitiful security of my *social security card*. Yet, not compensating this by a raise in salary.

The depth and the fury of my anger leaves me weak. But *Wednesday is rent day*, silences me. In a choked voice I answer meekly, "Yes Ma'm," and stagger out. The women gather around me, sympathetic but silent until we are out of her earshot. Then their anger finds its voice. "The s's of b's . . . the so and so. . . . For Christ? The devil, most likely." Hurriedly, in torrents of words, they pour out of their souls . . . for after all we must hurry back to work. There are only three hours left to finish the monstrous beds.

Listen, listen carefully, to those broken English words. For most of the women who utter them are *Catholics*. The hurried thumb-picture they give is one of stark horror and tragedy. Lives lived in hole-in-the-wall rooms for $1.50 a week, in overcrowded, fetid slums. Thin coats in the winter. Hand-me-down garments all the year round.

Inarticulate but powerful hates dance in these words of theirs. "The caissons are rolling along." Heavy caissons of human hate, of hunger for justice, flouted or denied.

Days, centuries—of beds, sheets, pillow-cases. After six hours of that type of work, *the rest is spent in getting over the utter exhaustion and bodily weariness.*

Then came the third day. The prim housekeeper came to our floor and announced that we would have to make more beds on another floor where a girl had left (no wonder she did).

Still chained by rent, and food we had to buy, we went . . . They and I went . . and *made thirty-four extra beds that day . . . seventy-nine beds in six hours . . . a bed every four and a half minutes.* An hour later, I found my companion, a widow, sobbing on a half-made bed. "Katzie, I can't, I just can't . . I ain't slept all night yesterday. My back, my feet ache something awful from this work. Oh! Katzie what is the use? I can't make the grade. It's the gas oven for me." That afternoon I finished my seventy-nine beds, and twenty of hers. I stayed longer on the job. But, I might as well tell you, I did not go near a church for three days. And I quit with just enough dough for rent. I did not eat much that week either. I just lay there in my brown hopeless room . . . hating with a hate that would kill. . . .

That is how it is . . . I'll close here tonight.

FIFTH LETTER

Dear Bishop

I have changed jobs again. Yes. Again. Got so tired of the "Christian" place with its seventy-nine beds that were more monstrous in their implications than all the machines in the world. Tired also of having Christ sold so blatantly, for the unseen, but real, thirty pieces of silver. You can take so much, and then, suddenly, you cannot take any more. Not at any price.

So I am working at Jensen's. Slinging hash again. Day work. From noon, really from 11:30 A.M. to 8 P.M. The usual eight hours. The kitchen is far. There is a lot of walking to do. The pay is not bad. Eighteen dollars a week, plus two meals and uniforms. The tips are lousy, it is true, and I still seem to have difficulties to make the necessary twenty-five dollars, which, with the free meals, give me that little margin of safety I spoke about. But then most girls living alone

47

almost always find it hard to make ends meet.
So that isn't anything new.

Nor is the set-up any different at Jensen's than
anywhere else. The same lecherous grabbings,
the same dirty jokes in the kitchen, the same old
drab stories. But by now it is an old, old story
to me. The only thing I still hate about it is to
witness, day by day, how it takes God's glow out
of the eyes of the young girls. And my gorge rises
at the thought that no one seems to bother to
try and keep the glow there. . . .

Tell me, would Christ stoop very low? Low
enough to reach me, Katzie of the drab streets
and backwash of a city? And call *me* to do some
of the work that nobody else seems to be doing?
I have to laugh. Sure, I know, it's a lot of hot air.
"Baloney," as Lill the head waitress would say.
Maybe, that dream of mine, and the fight I have
been putting up for survival and the right to call
my soul my own, and the faith within it, really
have gone to my head. But the other day I found
myself "preaching" to a gentleman. Me, Katzie
the Polack, a waitress in a cheap joint!

So I sling hash and watch the world go by . . .
right here in my booths. The other day four

young soldiers walked in, ordered and started talking to me. They explained that they were making a Gallup Poll survey of their own, that there were several hundred soldiers in the town who first started little bull sessions, then merged them into a big one. It was about what they were fighting for, and what kind of world there was going to be after the war was over. They had come to definite decisions too, only now they wanted to know what the working people of America were thinking and hoping for. So they organized themselves in parties of four, Investigators, reporters, call them what you like, they said, but there they were asking waitresses, taxi drivers, workers, porters, and so forth and so on, their opinions.

Seemed screwy to me, kind of . . . usually it is them that everyone interviews, not the other way around. But there they were. Young, eager, earnest, asking—"Come on Katzie . . . tell us what do you think." Something just broke inside of me. It was the first time anyone even thought of me—us—bothered to ask what I—we—think! Strange what such a simple human attitude can do to you!!! So I broke down and told them about the room, the fight, and the poverty, the worry about the rent, the foreman,

49

the cooks, the Church, the feeling most of us have, that no matter how it goes, we little people who work will never get a break. Above all I told them of the fear in my heart and the hearts of many of us . . . that another depression will come after the War and rob us of the last shreds of our human dignity. For that is what happened the last time . . .

As I spoke I knew my eyes were filled with tears. And I was ashamed, until I saw tears in theirs. They listened, as if I were the President himself, as if I, Katzie the Polack, were the most important thing in the world. And this did things to me again. Straightened my shoulders. Took the pain out of my back, arms and legs, that has been there, oh, for so long now. Just that. Someone asking, someone caring, someone listening. As simple as that.

Then they started to talk. They told me they read and study just the things I was telling them about. That they were ready to fight and die, but only if little people like me—us—might have the decencies of life. That, no matter, there were plenty of them who would come back and see that we did. They also said that this was the end of an era. That capitalism must go. That some form of socialism will take its place. That the only question was what type of socialism—Communistic or otherwise. That enough was enough. That they were ready to go on killing the bastards that opposed these ideas in the USA, or the world, and that this was the way all the workers felt. For, after all, the soldiers of the world were mostly workers. They added too, not to worry. They thought all these things would come peaceably, by discussion and evolution—not revolution.

But they langhed, a sort of bitter laugh, about the write-ups they were getting in the press. The "slushy ballyhoo," they called it. "Let it ride," one said, "it isn't our time yet."

They had it all at their finger tips. The food muddle. The need for reorganizing the unions. The counter plans of what they called the vested interests. All was there. And for each they were ready. Gee, more goes on in those "bull sessions" than one ever dreams of. They spoke of Communism soberly, simply, gave its good points, but dismissed it as unsuitable for the USA. I mentioned religion to them . . . and for the first time there was a silence. They looked at each other, and at me. There was a God, sure enough, they said . . .

Christ . . . He had been a worker, a champion of the oppressed. They believed in Him. But the *Churches—no.* And again they said No. And with that they dismissed the Church. All churches. Just like that. And don't forget that they were *four*, who represented several hundreds of our American youth. They were going to fight and die . . for something big and in their young, eager minds . . . it sure was not the Church. Yet, there was a day—I read about it, someplace—when *youth was dying for the Church! Why not now?*

And the two gents, that came in for breakfast last Sunday. One ordered a gin-sling. At 10 A.M. The other, just the regular breakfast. One drank steadily. The other feebly tried to keep him from doing so. The sober one talked to me. He said the other was his pal. He was going into the Army the next day, so he had been on a binge since two days ago. Did not see any reason why he should fight. They were college pals, he said. Graduated from a Catholic college. He understood his pal. There really was nothing in the present set-up to fight for, but he did not approve of his making a pig out of himself just because of that.

One thing led to another. And soon he was telling me his life-story. People are like that. It grows on you. And then one day you just can't take it . . . so you blurt it out to the Katzies of the world. It was a simple story at that. It started with the Beatitudes. The gent, and he was about 32, had been re-reading them, and came across the one about justice, and the hunger for it. So being a Catholic, he went in search of it. Searched well. For five or six years . . . and landed in the Communist Party.

He was an engineer. One of those with many letters after his name. All won in Catholic colleges. That's what got him in the end. The preaching, and the talking, and the *not* doing, as he put it. He went beserk there, some years back. Left the Church. And found what he was looking for in the "Comrades," or Communists. "Katzie" he said to me, "they jive. In whatever they teach, they jive—for they practice it."

We sobered his pal up. And Mr. Engineer, asked me for a date. I don't date customers as a rule. But this guy was wounded deep—*and the wounded don't wait.* So I went. I wish you had been there, to see the depth, width, and height of his wounds. He spent all Wednesday afternoon talking about himself . . . telling me, in between, that I should join the Party . . showing me, as only learned people can, that it had *all the answers I was seeking.* Would you believe it? The world rocked under my feet. And the face of Christ grew dim, as I listened over a cup of java, to the vibrant voice of a guy who had had a Catholic education since he was knee high until manhood, explain the Communist ideas to me. That is the way of it. Yet we finished the date in a Catholic church.

I did not know enough to argue with him, but I thought Christ did. So I challenged Mr. Engineer to come to church with me, and then tell it all over again to Him. He went, almost against his will, quite startled by my request. How do you explain what happened next? I can't explain it anyway. It was to Christ that I instinctively wanted to take him . . . for Christ alone could heal *his wounds.* We knelt there . . . in silence.

For how long I don't know. It was quiet. Peaceful like . . . and the Communists did not have a chance. The twilight came. A priest walked softly into the confessional. I looked up at the Engineer. He looked back at me. There were tears in his eyes. Silently he rose and went into the box. I prayed. It lasted a long, long time, that confession of his, but when he came out, he looked so different.

I had to go back, slinging hash. It was my evening on. So, I said good-bye. He went off to Washington that night. I guess I shall never see him again. But what of the other ninety-nine like him?

And the barber who comes daily for lunch at 3 P.M. Works in a place where there are only soldiers and sailors now for customers. He says that the revolution is here already. So far unbloody, but wait and see, when the boys come home. Many of them just talk of that. The new song of American youth, the barber calls it. He, too, wants me to join the Party. I would not hurt you that much, Bishop, as to tell you what he thinks of all of you. The words are unprintable. Yet he has a brother who is a priest.

In saloons, factories, hotels, restaurants . . . in the back alleys, in the kitchens of America, there is a mighty stirring of souls and minds. People talk, think, argue, seek, and even pray . . and the only ones always around to give the answers are the COMMUNISTS.

The storm is gathering. The lightning lights the skies. Against the darkness, youth marches to death in seried ranks, or makes merry in an effort to forget. But not for an instant does it *really* forget. The tragedy is that neither in its thinking, fighting, or making merry, *has the Church a great part.* And it could so easily *have* a part!

Tomorrow dawns, with the Son of Man still hanging on the Cross. And, seemingly, there is no one to take Him down. . . .

It is late now . . Good night, Bishop.

SIXTH LETTER

Dear Bishop

Just came back from work. In the twilight the room looks more drab than ever. Its brown dirt merges with the gray sky outside, a symphony of misery and hopelessness. There isn't enough light to really write by but write I must again. For thoughts, like flies against a screen on a summer day, buzz endlessly in my tired brain. Again the desire to run . . . to quit . . . to leave the Church is strong upon me. And I am too weary, to get up and go, and look at "my Christ" in the old Church in the next block.

I am still at Jensen's . . . going on the second week. The room rent is paid. There is enough change left to feed me the one extra meal I don't get there. But, I am, oh! so tired. Again my legs and feet ache, like an old familiar toothache . . . what's the use of going on living . . . if life is like this . . . Jensen's . . . my hopeless room? Jensen's or some other place like it? All for a mere pittance, that is not really enough to keep body and soul together.

The kitchen smells of stale frying oil, onions, and dirty dishwater. The four cooks look like the smells. The dishwasher looks worse. The Negro porter moves, slowly making a pretense of mopping a floor that should be scrubbed clean. His mop leaves dirty streaks. It is the lull hour of an afternoon. The lunch hour is over, the dinner rush, not yet here.

The waitresses gather for a smoke. Exchanging, lazily, dirty jokes with the male workers. The chef swears and goes on explaining that he is fed up with it all. He wishes, he adds, this damn war was over, so that the revolution would come. A waitress laughs and says that the money bags won't let any revolution come. Another bull session begins in the dirty kitchen of a joint called a "restaurant." Lazily at first, then with growing heat the arguments are thrown back and forth. The old theme-song. Again the depths of human hearts open. Again a glimpse of what poverty, grinding poverty, does to human souls is revealed. In a flash that blinds, Emma, the counter-waitress, asks me in a half whisper, what do I think . . . of a man . . . at ten dollars . . . a night?

And I find myself hesitating, then wondering "why not?" Sure, I know there is the Sixth Commandment, but figure it out for yourself. Emma is a widow. She has two kids. Eight and seven. She works the breakfast shift. From 5 A.M. to 2 P.M. so that she might be back for the kids to come from school. In the mornings a neighbor takes care of them. That means money. . . .

Well, with a lot of work at home and in our joint, she is just melting away, before your very eyes . . . and never enough money for the kids' shoes, clothes and what have you. And there are men, there always are men. Ten dollars is a lot of money, too, and there is no one to help her. There are many like her . . . in the back kitchens and factories of the land. Women like Emma, Catholics at that, who in moments of near despair, wonder if they should accept men for money, so their kids won't go hungry or half naked. That is the way of it.

The arguments have waxed rough. The second cook is all for the Russian way. Brandishing his big carving knife, he speaks with a suppressed fury of his and the working people's wrongs. Nothing but blood could wash these off, he says. Blood . . . the word brought memories, that were no memories at all . . . and yet were there . . . real, true, frightening. *The Precious Blood*, the blood of a dying God, that washed away all sin. All but the sins of those who refused it . . . refused it of their own free God-like will . . . given to them, by that same dying, crucified Lord!

There is no escaping *blood*. It comes closer and ever closer, that smell of blood.

Blessed are they that hunger for justice. They shall be filled. These solemn words echo and re-echo through all the centuries, bringing with them, on the eternal winds of the Holy Ghost, the smell of new grass and flowers from the Mount on which they were spoken. Portentous words . . . that have taken roots in men's hearts . . . and changed the face of the earth. . . .

For by implication they spell also the reverse. Cursed are they who neither hunger for, nor dispense, justice . . . they shall perish from a hunger not of this world!

Bishop, the world, my world of cooks, waitresses, factory girls, porters, dishwashers . . . the same as those who sat and listened in rapture to Christ on the Mount . . . is crying out for justice and receiving no answer from those who have been sent to give it to them . . . so they feel like searching for it with kitchen knives and hatchets.

The first cook agrees with the second. The Negro leaning on his dirty mop shakes his head vigorously, mumbling over and over again, "Yes, sir, yes man, them is true words . . ." The dishwasher suddenly breaks his silence spitting out, "Them sons of bitches . . . let me at their throats and I'll show them . ."

In the silence that follows, hate hangs poised in the air, making it hard to breathe. I venture a timid reminder that there are other ways than killing, to get the same results; that Christ showed it to us. But the chorus of ridicule that assails me on all sides . . by its sheer, noisy weight, silences me. Again, I am confronted with the accomplished fact that neither the

Church, nor Churchmen, nor even Christ, have a place in the plans of these people—people He came to save . . . nor their future. What kind of future will it then be . . . without Him? At this moment I catch a strange glimpse of the state of Judas' soul . . . before he went back to the priests, trying to return their silver. . . .

The doors are opened with a bang. The boss wants to know who in hell do we think we are. Customers outside. And we sitting on our fannies doing nothing. It's my turn. I go and take an order. It is just a young girl. She is in her teens. She orders a gin fizz . . . at three in the afternoon!! I bring it to her. She starts to talk. Another one of the army of lonely youth.

The tale is stale. Pearl Harbor. Excitement. Men in uniforms. Fire in her blood. Recklessness. A desire for sacrifice, that no one guides. A soldier. A dreary hotel room. A baby in the making. Abortion. Soldier gone. Other soldiers. And she is only seventeen. And now gin-fizzes at three in the afternoon! To forget? Or to remember? Nothing but a void and a loneliness that makes her talk to waitresses.

I listen, my back against the wall of the booth. Mary of Magdala, pray for her. Gently I point out the mercy, the understanding of God, the hope of youth. Explain that nothing is lost. That the road is clear ahead. That it was only a stumble, a fall, a slight bruise. She looks up, eyes full of tears, the gin-fizz untasted. Now she is up . . . kisses me on the cheek with a whispered "thank you." A bill thrust hurriedly into my hand. She is gone.

How many of them are filling our big city streets tonight? Who will have time to listen to them?

The place begins to fill up. Dishes, full at first— then empty. A chain of dishes. Food, and more food . . . laughter . . . tears . . . comedy . . . drama. All around me. Here are three soldier boys . . . earnestly talking about the war. They think they know what they are fighting for . . . the four freedoms. Until a sailor walks in on them and picks each of their arguments to smithereens. It hurts me to see their bewilderment . . . the hurt looks on their boyish faces.

The woman alone. Just lost a son. Last casualty list had his name. She just sits there. And asks "why, why, why?" in a dead monotone. I speak hurriedly of Christ, between two orders of fried ham and eggs for the next booth. She answers, "There is no God." When I come back with the hamburgers for booth five, she is gone. A lull again. We who work now eat at the counter. A bus driver and a taxi man sit by. The conversation of every American these days turns on the "to-morrow" after the war. Oh, why does everyone propound a plan in which God is not included? What has been left undone, that Americans of 1943 don't know the Son of Man?

It is late. The sky outside is dark. Time I stopped writing. Good-night.

SEVENTH LETTER

Dear Bishop

I am back in my old saloon. The one I started at when I began to write these letters. It happened this way. I was passing by it and went in to say hello. It wasn't even funny. The "girls" all greeted me like a long lost friend. The bartender put up drinks on the house. Everyone in chorus explained that they had missed me. And the boss came out and asked me to come back. The waitress they had after me was no good, he said. He had to throw her out right in the middle of a busy night. She swore and drank with customers and raised hell everywhich way. Would I come back? He offered me a raise. I said I would, and did the next day. I have been there over a week now. It is not easy, yet it is easier than all my other jobs. Because I am treated like a human being. True, mostly by people whom others consider as having surrendered all rights to their respect. But, it helps just the same.

Grace now. You remember Grace? The Catholic who graduated from a Catholic college? We have had many more talks since I came back. And Grace is out of the saloon. She is on a decent, important war job now. As she puts it, "Katzie, I am respectable again. I can look people straight in the face. Never hide from my mother again. You know what? One of these days I will go back to Church. Why should I stay away from God, because, years back, a priest dimmed His face for me?" So Grace is OK now, perhaps, because she had a waitress to talk to, one who has not yet completely lost her way. . . .

Ginette . . you remember Ginette? The one I dared not tell you about? Well, she and I have been talking things over too. Last week she gave the guy the gate. For I persuaded her that the "strange feeling" she confessed she had about him was nothing but the grace of God . . . hers through Baptism, that she could not erase, no matter what her attitude to the Church. So she has given him the gate. I am glad. She is a long, long way from "home" yet. She laughs a

66

high, strident laugh every time I mention confession.

Yet she herself brought me a holy picture with a, "Here Katzie, ain't she sweet?" It was a gaudy picture of Our Blessed Lady. Gaudy or not . . . Ginette liked her. And then she asked me to pray for her the other day. Will you say a prayer for Ginette too, please?

I have lost track of Gwendolyne, Jean, Helene. But someday, if I look long enough I will find them again, God willing. Then there is Joe the bartender. Irish Catholic. The other day he was saying that maybe he would organize himself and drop into church, it being Lent . . . what with the war and things. But I don't know if he will. If only there were someone, a priest, a Catholic layman, who could, sort of, talk to him about it, in-between two beers, friendly like . . . Then maybe. . . .

Patrick is six feet two or three inches tall. Solid flesh too. A policeman . . . not a plainclothes man. Patrick thinks I've got "IT" Sex appeal. Patrick is used to our musty, blowsy street . . . its liquor, its women, its graft. All come to him for the asking, the stretching of a hand, the raising of an eyebrow. Pat has been on the street, many years. Irish, he gets his way. So his first embrace, casual as it was, was also indecent. Why should a cop be decent to Katzie the Polack, waitress in a backwash saloon? No reason. Gently I took his hands off. How weary I am of men's hands! Only God knows. But they seem to go with the kind of jobs that are mine.

I was not angry. Instead I asked him about his faith. Startled at first, he hid his astonishment behind a grin. "Mick . . . that is what I am, a Mick, Katzie, and a lousy one at that." Still gently, I asked him about the Sixth Commandment. He looked at me, "Faith, Katzie, you sound like a nun I knew." I explained that I was a Catholic too, and that I did not like that kind of pawing. I reminded him of Lent. Asked if he had done his Easter duty. "Naw, not for a couple of years," he muttered. Then he suddenly asked me if I would have a bite to eat with him after work. I agreed. We went. We sat there and talked over a cup of coffee. . . . And Pat has made his Easter duty. It can be done.

Saturday night is hectic in my streamlined saloon. The Armed forces come in crowds with their girl friends. All so hopelessly, helplessly, young. They drink a little, dance, and make love. In booths and on the floor, for me, the night is hellish. Not a minute to sit down. Nine solid hours of running all over. Slinging drinks endlessly in a fetid atmosphere of swearing, sweating, raucous laughter. Drunks . . . plus lust . . . against thick cigarette smoke in the air. Cigarettes and whiskey . . . all stale. Like most people around me.

Midnight. One A.M. My feet ache. My back aches. My soul and heart weep and cry out into the void of a saloon. Two-thirty . . . I am dizzy with fatigue. And faint with hunger, for there was no time even for a bite. Four kids in a booth, on whom I have kept an eye through the night. I always do. There are so many. I kid them along, and stop them from drinking too much. These noticed how white and tired I looked . . . and said so. Mechanically, I answered that I was dead beat, and there was Mass still to go to. At three o'clock. The only Mass I could take in. The four youngsters looked startled. At me and at each other.

"Why Katzie, you go to Mass, after all this work? Then we will go too!" The next booth, four more kids heard that, and joined in the conversation stating that they too were Catholics. Four soldiers and four girls and I knelt in the old church that morning. As I went to Communion, a strange thing happened. I was not tired at all.

Being a restless sort of a person and a curious one, I circulate much. I am therefore thoroughly "at home" in that strange tight world of my blowsy street. So small geographically and so big spiritually! Cops know me and say "hello" as I go by. The workers of other "joints" stop to pass the time of day and exchange a bit of gossip. So do those who work in the burlesque shows, as well as the tattoo man, and the owner of the cheap peep-show down the street. Even the merchants. I am on the inside of my little world, looking out . . . and you are on the outside looking in. That is a start. I can tell you all about it, because I firmly believe you're listening . . . and some day, I also believe . . . from my telling, and your listening . . . help will come to us on the blowsy street.

There was Lucky. A healthy, hefty youngster. She still is around. The day she came to celebrate her 18th birthday, with a guy twenty years older, and drank so many Kesslers and sweet

sodas that she was "not all there," is the day
I remember best. That day she showed me a
medal of St. Christopher on a long silver chain.
Some priest had given it to her. It was also the
day her gent wanted me to make a hotel reser-
vation for a double bedroom for "Mr. and Mrs.
Smith." He said it with a smirk too. I got real
mad and told him to go to hell and make his
own reservations. He did. While he was phon-
ing, I tried to argue with Lucky. She smiled
drunkenly and said, "Oh Katzie, what the hell,
I lost my virginity when I was twelve, and I am
eighteen today. Too late to worry about it now.
I am out for some fun." I pleaded and coaxed,
but got nowhere, as far as I could see. They
walked out, arm in arm, into the night.

All that evening and the next day I felt lousy.
Yesterday, Lucky returned and smilingly shoved
into my hand a receipted bill for a single room
in a woman's hotel. "See, Katzie, I was not too
drunk to listen. And what you said about the
Blessed Mother crying over me got me. So I gave
the guy the gate. Give us a kiss for that, eh Katzie, my pal . ."

Since then my saloon has been OK by me. And
even my room ain't so drab anymore.

EIGHTH LETTER

Dear Bishop

The Saloon is OK with me, maybe! When the Luckies who drift in for something they call "fun," suddenly realize, at the brink of an abyss that this is not fun, but sin. . . . Or again when the Graces and Gladyses leave it for God's sunshine. But it is not this way always. I still have to write to you, because, if I stop, the sheer weight of the countless, unanswered questions within me, will hurl me too, into the abyss.

My room is still brown and dark. The dust and noise of the street are still with me. What if I scrub, wash, and try oh so hard to make it cozy? It is still all I have to live in. Can I wash away its strange, closed-in smell? The ghosts of the hundreds of anonymous people who lived in it? The strange shadows of backwash streets . . . spawns of the Big City's sins, that haunt me day and night? Can I wash away, with soap

and water, the sight and the memories of the
pinched and tired faces of all the girls who lived
in the room next to me? They came and they
went. Men came to them and disappeared,
stealthily, into the night. Shadows on the screen
of life. Maybe! Unimportant ones at that.
Maybe! But not to God. No, soap and water
will not wash *that* off. You see, I *live* here. Day
in and day out. *The saloon . . . and this . . . this
and the saloon . . .* shuttling back and forth . . .
between two hells. Yes, I have to keep on writing to you . . or hell will close in on me.

So let us talk about youth today. The youth of
America, that passes on in a continual stream
and sooner or later lands at my Saloon. Mine
and thousands like mine. I know you *are* interested in youth. You have proven it a thousand
ways. Youth, the hope of the world, the harvest
of the church . . its very foundation. Youth in
civilian clothes . . youth in the khaki of the
Army . . the blue of the Navy, the olive-drab
of the Marines . . . draftees . . . farmers, they
come to us, in an unending stream.

Why? Could it be that they enjoy the dim lights,
the hot, gay music of the Negro band, the com-

panionship of the girls unsupervised, uncensored, of their *own* choice? Come with me, while I serve drinks. I listen to them, eight hours every night of the week, except on my day off: I see them act naturally . . . "Take their hair down" . . . hold their bull sessions, undisturbed, in peace . . . being at long last, just *themselves.*

Do they talk? *Endlessly.* Straight from the shoulder. You sure can get an earful, just by standing there, listening. But no one does. The bartender is bored. Just "kids" talking, and they buy only a couple of beers at best. The "B" girls keep away from them. No money there. Once in a while, one will accept a drink from them. Kiss them lightly. Stay in a booth for a moment or two. Mostly because she feels sorry for them, and is patriotic in her own fashion.

So "the boys" talk. Listen to music. Laugh a little. Kid a little. *But above all they talk.* Not even noticing the M.P.'s or S.P.'s, who wander in and out of the place dutifully, but with a bored air. The youngsters are well behaved, for the most part. Anyhow, can a military, or special policeman see the banked fires in a guy's mind and soul? Thanks be to God—not yet.

74

But I am frightened, listening to them. I find myself wishing that they would be angry with the Church. But no, they won't even pay her the compliment of anger. They ignore her. She just isn't there. *To think that the Church Christ died establishing has no place in the soul of this section of American youth, nor shares in the building of its future. . . . Why this is sheer tragedy!*

But come closer. Listen in, to what youth in and out of the armed forces talks, thinks and really feels in this year of grace.

The door opens; and, with the cold wind, come gusts of gay laughter and a snatch or two of a popular tune, brought in by a group of sailors. They seem to fill the place, though they are but ten or twelve. They order a round of beers and pile in a booth. Soon they are deeply engrossed in conversation. No one pays any attention to them. They feel at home. There is only me, Katzie the waitress, to listen to them, and they don't mind me. I am a part of the furniture to them. Once in a while they might even turn to me for a confirmation, or for a question or two, and then go on with their bull session.

The tall dark sailor, with the eagle face, holds forth. His subject? Always the same: *What are we fighting for?* He has the full attention of his listeners. A rapt attention. In the dimness of the room, their faces look strained, pale, yet full of an inner fire. A better world, that is what the dark sailor was ready to die for . . . if it came. But he did not see how it could, if things went on as they were going. Millions were still in poverty, he pointed out, right here in the USA. And after the war, they would be worse off. *That could not, must not, happen.* Someone wanted to know how he could prevent it. He told them in answer the story of the Russian Revolution. The "glorious" role played by the sailors in it. That was the way. *His way, anyhow.*

A slight blond lad mentioned the four freedoms as a fighting goal. At once bedlam broke loose. They all spoke at once, interrupting each other. Slowly a modicum of order was restored. They took each "freedom" in turn. *The Freedom of the Press* came first. Everyone laughed. It was not a pleasant laugh. For they evidently did not believe in that freedom, these youngsters of mine. Not as a thing to fight or die for in its present state, anyhow. In the picturesque language of modern youth, they disposed of it in short, snappy sentences like these:

"Freedom of the Press? Hell no. With every damn newspaper in the country chained to the circulation desk, vested interests, and political powers? Naw, we ain't dying for the Press that thinks the guy of 57 varieties is more important than Katzie, the waitress here. *The truth and nothing but the truth?* It's a laugh. All these sheets would not know the truth if they saw it. And if one did know it, it would not touch it with a ten-foot pole. Afraid of stepping on some gouty toes. Free Press? That's a hot one." *Thus summarily one of the Four Freedoms was dismissed by youth on its way to die.*

Freedom of Religion. They had no quarrel with that. Nor any interest in it either. The discussion lagged at this point. As if no one thought religion worth dying for. As if they wondered why anyone bothered to insert it as a reason to fight and die for. Again the eagle-faced sailor spoke. "Sure; let it be. For those weaklings that need or want it. But for me? What has religion ever done for me that I should die for it? Its OK in its place, especially for women folks.

But it ain't important." That settled it. No one in that group, anyhow, argued the point. No commentaries were made. No sparks flew. The word that had set the world on fire, started crusades, changed worlds and civilizations, did not even ruffle the surface of a group of American youths in the year of grace 1943. Dead? Maybe. Only . . . I want to know . . . can something die, that did not exist . . . for them?

Freedom of Speech? Oh, yes, they were willing to die for that. They saw its splendors and its force. They saw that without it men's minds and souls would languish and die. Again unanimous agreement, but ardent and loud and passionate this time.

Freedom from Want. That is where they started to go to town. Just like the workers in my old factory. Their eyes sparkled and shone. Their words, clumsy and youthful, became almost prophetic, though they were not aware of it. *Freedom from want . . . for themselves . . . their children . . . and the world's youth and peoples. . . .* And now they all again spoke at once. Oh, how I wish I had the gift of writing. To put on paper their fire, their anger, their hopes!

Each interrupted the other, to prove his point, to tell a tale of personal tragedy, poverty and shame. For most of them, were "Depression children." Their fists were clenched. Their young faces were set in ugly lines, as they "remembered" their blighted childhood. Do the "powers that are" realize *the depth and the width of the wounds youth bears on its heart and soul? The wounds seared deep by those ten shameful years . . . when those they loved . . . humiliated and beaten . . . stood in endless lines before welfare offices . . . government and religious alike . . . and bared their innermost lives so that their children might eat the crumbs so grudgingly given by the richest country in the world to its children . . . grudgingly given, sometimes, even in the name of Christ. No wonder they have learned to forget Him, not even to associate His Holy Name with a charity that was hard and cold. . . .*

Someone mentioned Russia again. A little silence fell on the group. A silence of respect and admiration. Russia's case has not failed for want of people to state it. There was a lull in their arguments, not unlike the sound-filled short silence between two parts of a symphony.

I was silent too, with a silence of utter pain and sorrow. The sentiment of all was expressed by the youngest sailor, one with the face of a child. *"Yep, for this I am willing to die, all right . . . that people like Katzie here, and the likes of her all over the world . . . should have freedom from want. . . . And remember, buddies, when I say fight and die, I mean everywhere . . . in foreign lands . . . and also right here, in these United States of ours . . . Like the Russian sailors did. Katzie, bring us another round of beer. . . . . . .*

Suddenly, as fast as it had begun, the bull session was over. Girls came. And the sailors danced, sang, and laughed.

NINTH LETTER

Dear Bishop

The other day I read in the Gospels about Christ going into the desert, to pray and fast for forty days. I had heard and read this story before many times. But, then, suddenly, I, Katzie of the backwash streets, understood clearly, sharply and fully the word "desert." Saw it vividly, with a shock to my soul that left me weak and panting. Why *I* was in a desert. All those about me *permanently lived there*. A desert? Yes, I knew it for what it was!!! A fearful, lonely place . . . immense . . . without bread or water . . . killing men's souls, minds, hearts, bodies . . . making them a pack of animals. They were seeking to escape . . . running hither, thither, and yon . . . only to fall back exhausted, before the endless infinite horror of the desert.

Dirty, run-down streets . . . multiplied over and over again in America . . . arid deserts. Foxholes. With men, women, and kids, living in them. In filth, cold, and darkness . . . or in heat and dust. Thousands of them. Forgotten, unknown, anonymous. Lonely, poor, starved for light, sunshine and love. Saharas of our modern, refined, civilization.

Yes, in a flash I understood. Christ suffered from thirst. We do too. Thirst of Him . . . of and for the eternal waters of Truth. He was hungry. So are we . . . for the Bread of Eternal life. He was tempted by Lucifer . . . so are we, constantly. *He knew about us,* beating our bloody fists against an unseen wall that cuts us off from our most precious heritage . . . *His Truth.* I saw it all in a flash and knew His passion encompassed our pain . . . our loneliness and hopelessness. He was "us". . . the men, women and kids of all these forgotten streets. And I knew more . . . He was still here . . . only our eyes were dimmed by tears, hunger, and thirst . . . and so we lose our way . . . again and again.

OH! Christ of the desperate, have mercy on us. . . . Come speak to us Yourself, as you did to the woman taken in adultery. Come, Lord of Hosts, Son of a Carpenter, come . . . and give us

82

over again Your sermon on the Mount. Where
we live there is no Mount, except of the refuse
of a big city. There is no grass . . . only hard,
dirty pavements. But we, the poor, the "little
ones" of today, we shall listen and understand,
as did those of your yesterdays, the words of
Life. And understanding, we will not mind poverty, hunger and thirst. We will not even feel
these ills, for our souls will forever reflect the
glory of Your face, and our hearts hear the echo
of Your voice. Come, Christ of the Workers.
Come Yourself, for we are lost in the desert of
briars and thorns. Come, Jesus, Come. . . .

That is the way my soul cried out to the Lord,
Bishop, in my dark room . . . and I am not
ashamed to tell you about it, for I am well-
nigh reaching the end of the road. Lately I am
weary . . . in soul and mind and heart. The will
to live . . . to go on . . . is slowly ebbing from me.
I had to cry out to the Lord, for I am but a creature and cannot take "His desert" as He did.
Faith and Hope, the cardinal virtues, seem to
die slowly, like flowers die, in my soul.

Anger, the like of which I have never known,
shakes me as in a fever. Pity and Charity for

those with whom I share all this, alone hold me up. Great, dry sobs rise within me. I wish I could be all the things they need. But it needs the Sacrament of Ordination for mortals to become "all things to all men"—doesn't it? Trapped. That's what I am. Trapped like a rat. Besieged from all sides by a million mouths that shout, day and night . . . night and day. "What of Justice? God's Justice? What of Charity, whose other name is Love? God's Love. What of His teachings? What of the dignity of man? The right to live, to work, to marry, to the pursuit of happiness? What of feeding the hungry, clothing the naked, giving drink to the thirsty? *What of . . . what of . . . what of?* Their mouths shout at me. Their eyes shout at me. I even hear the futile cries of their hopelessly-bound souls. . . .

Oh, yes, I still shuttle between my saloon and my fox-hole. I was there last Tuesday. The place was half empty. Seven soldiers were sitting at the bar, nursing some beer. Their conversation was at first slow and desultory until one started to define Democracy. The thing they are supposed to be fighting for. In no time it became apparent that they all agreed on only one thing. They could not fight for Democracy, because there wasn't any in the USA to fight for. But they thought that they could do a thing or two to remedy this when they came back, after having attended to the primary and all-important job of winning this war. They would hold on to their rifles. Yep, they would do that; and there would be a new political party, a "Soldier's Party." The Legion was powerful after the last war, they conceded, but it would be peanuts, to what they would be. *Peanuts*. Because they were ready to fight for the right to live decently. Fight street by street. House by house. Field by field. Right here at home.

They said their say and looked grim and resolute, as only youth can look. The bartender, an old veteran, shook his head mournfully and remarked that it was all very well, but the big wigs, who held money and power in this land, were wise guys too. And making ready even now.

For one thing, the demobilization would be slow. Little contingents would trickle back. Rifles would be taken away, before you could say "knife." Oh no, the youngsters answered. Not this time. Because it was not something that they alone wanted. It was something *all the soldiers of the world, all the workers of the world, wanted. And that made it different from last time.* If the big wigs, the world over, did not see the writing on the wall, they would get a World Revolution that would be a *World Revolution.*

At the very end of the bar sat a lone soldier. Straight, thin, young. He had been silent through all the discussion. Now when a strange and almost uncomfortable silence had fallen on all of us, even the "B" girls, he spoke. In a soft, cultured voice. Slowly. As if choosing the right words. He told us that force was wrong. That the reason for all this mess we were in, was that we had forgotten God and His Commandments. That the thing to do was to support the Pope, His Peace and Social Justice program. He quoted the Labor Encyclicals. He called, like a prophet of old, for the cleansing of souls and hearts.

Alas, the words of this soldier fell on dry ground. The others listened respectfully. They always do to each other. Then they answered. You should have heard them! One boy spoke of the slums he had come from. Described the tenements he had grown up in. Added that it was owned by pious Catholics.

Another took up the tale from there. Vividly, succulently, and blasphemously, he described his own and his family's "tortures" (that is what he called it) by religious social agencies. He himself, through the depression, was "handled" by *fourteen of them*. Hate was in every glance of his. Hate shook his slight frame, that even the Army had not yet succeeded in filling up. The next one spoke. He was from the country. Way back in the drought States. A born Catholic. His words were venom. Since he was ten, neither he nor his family had set foot in a church. The Pope? That was rich! What did the Pope understand of poverty, degradation, insecurity? All priests preached the Sixth Commandment alone, to people who either did not even have the strength to sin against it, or had only the pleasures of the flesh to forget the horrors of daily life.

Of what the Church has to give her children in the spiritual order, this boy, clearly, hadn't a notion.

The slim young soldier with the quiet voice—
who, it turned out later, was a Catholic graduate
from Villanova College in the East—tried to tell
him. But the crowd came back at him, with
words like machine-gun bullets. He fought val-
iantly, but to no avail. *Christ's peace, so full of
pity, understanding, and love for these men,
seemed forever obscured from their sight by the
memories of Catholics in high places, whom they
had not liked. These soldiers could not see
through all these the face of a dying God—dying
for them in an utter surrender of love.*

Tears welled in the eyes of the boy from Villanova. He stood up, with his back against the
bar, drew himself up to his full height, and
spoke in a loud voice that brought silence again
to the whole room. "OK, you say the Bishops,
the priests have failed us. Perhaps some of them
have. So did Judas and Peter fail the Master.
But don't let us leave Christ out. Let us hold on
to Him. Let us die for Him, if we must. For the
same things He died for—*Justice to all. Brother-
hood of all men under the fatherhood of God.*
For if we don't, then *we die in vain . . .*"
Abruptly, he sat down, exhausted.

The silence lasted. Palpable. A living thing. No one moved. The flame of the Holy Ghost must have descended on my saloon. The beating of His wings could be heard. It was shattered again by words, like a glass can be shattered by sounds . . . "Keep your shirt on, Buddy, God is OK by us. Just you wait. We ain't atheists . . . but when we come back . . . them fellows in their black suits and upside down collars, are going to do an honest day's work . . . or we will know why!"

The boy from Villanova took his hat and walked out. Unsteadily. He had tried hard. He thought he had failed. He had not really. For after he left they argued some more, reaching the conclusion that there was a God, that He had to be included in their fights and plans. That He would understand their stand . . . a revolution, a fight for the modicum of necessities they felt were theirs by right . . . I wish I could find the Villanova soldier and tell him that.

"When I go to a ball . . . I have no trouble at all . . . The chicks that I pick are all tender, slender and tall . . ." The Negro band was playing and singing. Drowning out the words and voices of youth.

"God . . . Church . . . Justice . . . Rights . . . Priests . . . War." Ideas mixed strangely with the sax and the drum blended with the piano, but not for long.

Good nite Bishop!

TENTH LETTER

Dear Bishop

Monday, Tuesday, Wednesday . . . week days and Sundays . . . I have lost count of the days. They all seem alike to me. Sleep . . . work . . . a few little hours between, to wash my clothes, and mend them . . . the deadly routine between my saloon and my room. Deadly in its killing monotony of variety . . . and sameness.

Calverts and Cokes . . . Three beers . . . Make it two Cuba Libras . . . Four of same, coming up . . . "If you are not in love with someone else, why don't you fall in love with me?" "Go through that door . . . and to the right, as other women do, and bring me some money too.". . . Sentimental, slushy, hot, lusty . . . the cheap canned music from a juke box, or played by third-rate bands . . . goes on all night . . . melodious refrains to sin and despair . . . to forgetfulness that will not come . . . beating against my tired brain . . . torturing my soul, already tortured beyond endurance. "A pink cocktail for a blue "Lady"—"Honey-Hush." Boys in uniforms breaking their hearts in loneliness to these strange tunes . . . youth settling to-morrow without God, against the hot beat of boogey-woogey . . . Dark booths reveal what they hide. . . . Depths of sin are punctuated by the slow rhythms of the music.

I want to run . . . to hide . . . to become deaf and dumb and blind. . . . Two Calverts and Cokes. . . . "Lord, where are you?" Make mine beer. . . . "Mother of God, have pity on us!" Four Pabsts, and make it snappy. . . . "Son of Man and God, have you deserted us?"

"See me, girlie? Well, I and my buddies here ain't fit to associate with civilized people." He was one of the four soldiers who had come in grimly, half an hour ago, and had been sitting in a booth, drinking Scotch straight, without chasers of any kind. They were paratroopers. His friends tried to stop him. He brushed them off. He went on, in a dead monotone. "See us? We are not supposed to have leaves. Want to

know why? 'Cause we have been taught thirty-
two ways of killing our fellow human beings
with our bare hands and we've just started.
There are, they say, a hundred other ways. . . .
Take you. I could kill you now, by yanking your
windpipe out—just with them two hands of
mine. So you see, if we go on leave, and there
is a guy we had a grudge against back home,
well we are liable to settle it. Just like that. So
when this damn war is over, we all who come
back—we'll be experts . . . *experts in murder!*"

"What's your name? Katzie? That means Katie.
That is a nice name. My sister is Katie too. You
know what, Katie? I used to go to Sunday School
and sing in a choir. I was even an altar boy!
Now ain't that funny? Why don't you laugh,
fellows? Katie, why don't you? Remember 'Turn
the other cheek,' God said that. But our sergeant says, 'Now, boys you forget all that mush,
the golden rule . . . fair play. That is OK in
peace time. Now—you've got to kill or be killed,
and everything, every hold, goes.' Bring me another shot. To hell with the chaser, Katie . . .
Yep, I've got to forget everything I ever learned
about being decent. Yep, Katie when I come
back, do you think I will be able to sell insur-

ance again . . . or jerk sodas . . . marry . . . settle down? Gee, that IS rich! Me settle down after being like a beast for years. And there are thousands of us, Katie . . . thousands who have learned how to kill men with our BARE HANDS."

"Well," interjected another, "We have to give as we are given." With a suppressed fury, the first turned and snarled. "Shut up, you son of a bitch. Shut up, I say. . . . Don't you see? I-we have lost everything, because we have lost God. Look at me. Well, Katie . . . you see a man before you who has lost God. Bring me another shot."

"The chickens I pick are slender, tender, and tall." The band moaned, the sax seconded it *And I stood there looking at a man who had lost God.*

There was another soldier. Little John, they called him affectionately. He seemed smaller than most soldiers, but was like a little bantam cock. Full of spirits, energy and fight. I came up to serve him and his six buddies when they too were deep and hot on an argument about chap-

94

lains. Little John was saying that he had just come back from Florida, that there were units there that had no chaplains. He said it was the fault of the Bishops. That is unjust you say, Bishop. Of course it is unjust. But they're saying it and they needn't be—if a contact existed, they've broken it. They can't remake it by themselves. They don't even want to. And it's going to take a terrible lot of re-making.

Hear how he went on talking. "Oh, what the hell! Who needs the Padres anyhow? The Church is dead! We all believe in God, and that is enough."

My desert closed around me again. Suffocating me with its dust and heat. Not enough chaplains for the Armed Forces, as they see it. No one caring about the workers, right where the workers are . . . My backwash, blowsy streets. A wilderness waiting for a new sort of missionary. Shades of Father Marquette, Father Jogues, and all the martyred Jesuits! who is to follow in your footsteps?

Bishop, I have finished. There will be no more letters from Katzie. She has had her say. She has brought you the cry of men for God. You your-self, long ago, heard the cry of the God-Man for love and for souls. It must have been His "I thirst" that brought you where you are now. There is nothing I can add to what you know . . . or to what I told you. I shall go on carrying the cross of my knowledge . . . in peace, because I have shared it with you. *More I cannot do. Pray for me, that I shall retain my faith. And I shall pray for you.*

Goodbye, Bishop. May God have mercy on both our souls.